SUNDAY EXPRESS & DAILY EXPRESS

CARTOONS

Forty-second Series

AN EXPRESS BOOKS PUBLICATION

© 1988 Express Newspapers p.l.c., Fleet Street, London, EC4P 4JT

Printed in Great Britain by Purnell Book Production Ltd., Paulton, Bristol

FOREWORD

by

JOHNNY SPEIGHT

Screenwriter extraordinary

The gift to see us and point it out with wit and humour, that touch that very few have to mirror what we are. A talent to draw and bring to life . . . not only to draw but to know what to draw . . . Plus . . . that great touch . . . the "common touch" . . . the rare ability to reach right across the board. He spots our funny shapes, the nose that doesn't quite fit, the eyebrows that look more like moustaches, and his women who look more like men . . . those faces we see in every crowd, those awful relations, those awful neighbours . . . and those cats who look far more elegant and superior in shape than their owners and seem to know it. I could go on but they only want a paragraph.

Many, like me, I'm sure, would buy the EXPRESS just for "GILES".

The "DAILY EXPRESS" has had many great editors, and even more great writers but only one "GILES".

I've known him now for a good few years and have a strong suspicion he is Grandma.

Johnny Speight

"They've found Grandma — half way across the Atlantic on top of Concorde."

(Headline: A grandmother flies top of Tiger Moth for charity)

Daily Express, June 30th, 1987

"Mrs Thatcher didn't like being called only a housewife. Nor did my wife."

(Headline: French Prime Minister accuses Mrs. Thatcher of 'Housewife politics')

Daily Express, July 2nd, 1987

"Far corner, Martina Navratilova to serve —FORE"

Sunday Express, July 5th, 1987

"I can't see any of our cricketers leaping through the crowd to cuddle their daddies!"

(Headline: Tennis champion leaps from net to cuddle father)

Daily Express, July 7th, 1987

"Don't know why Prince Andrew objects to his wife's nickname 'Fergie', I never object to everyone calling you 'Fozzie Bear'."

"'What's the hurry, Mansell?' was fair comment for 95 in a 40 limit. Calling them gun-happy cowboys was not quite so witty."

"One usually sprays one's opponent AFTER he's won — not before he tees off."

Daily Express, July 14th, 1987

"I wish she WOULD—just to put your Mother's mind at rest"

Daily Express, July 16th, 1987

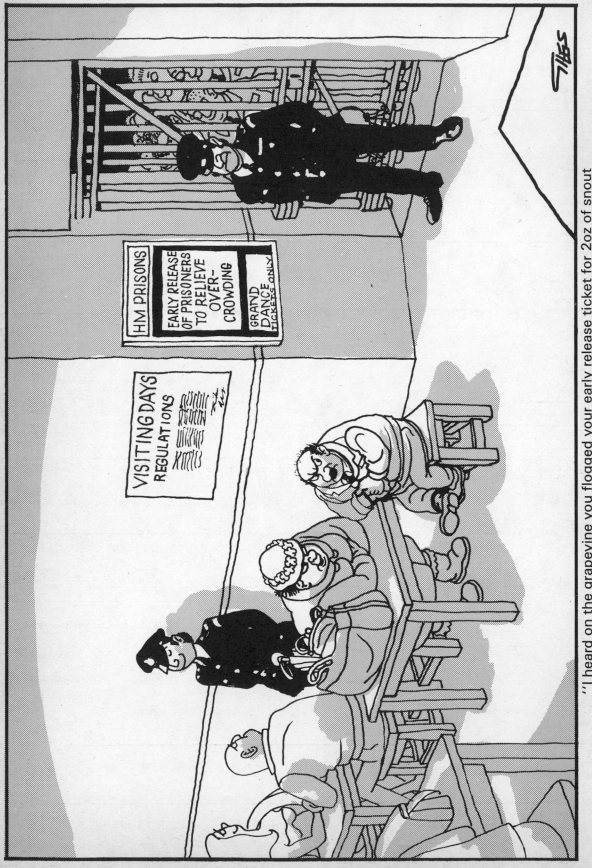

"I heard on the grapevine you flogged your early release ticket for 2oz of snout rather than come home to me and the kids."

Sunday Express, July 19th, 1987

"I've had her all the way from my house—"I didn't vote for you to vote yourself a rise to take three months' holiday in the Bahamas""

"Should any of you think of making minor alterations on the way home, photo-copies have been sent to all your parents."

Daily Express, July 23rd, 1987

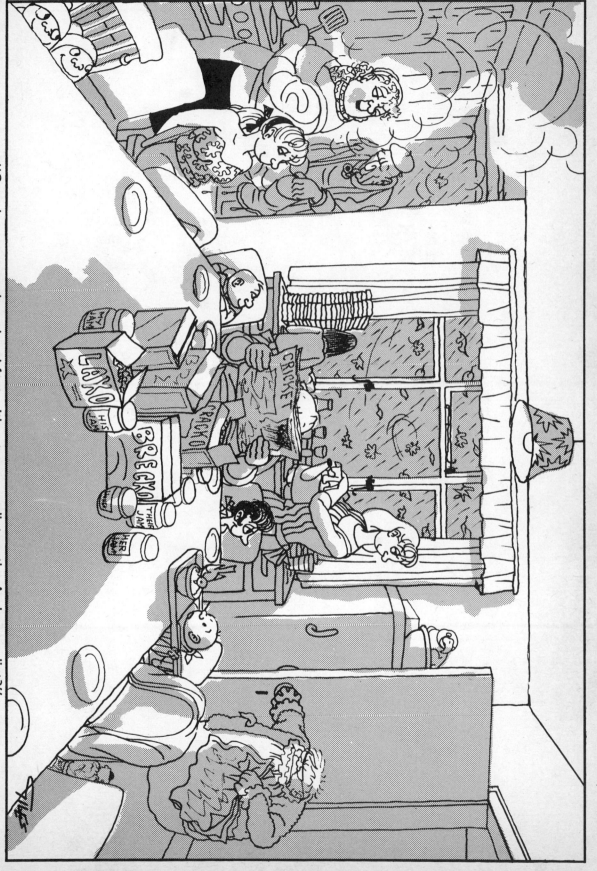

"Grandma, can we have breakfast without your verdict on the Archer verdict?"

Sunday Express, July 26th, 1987

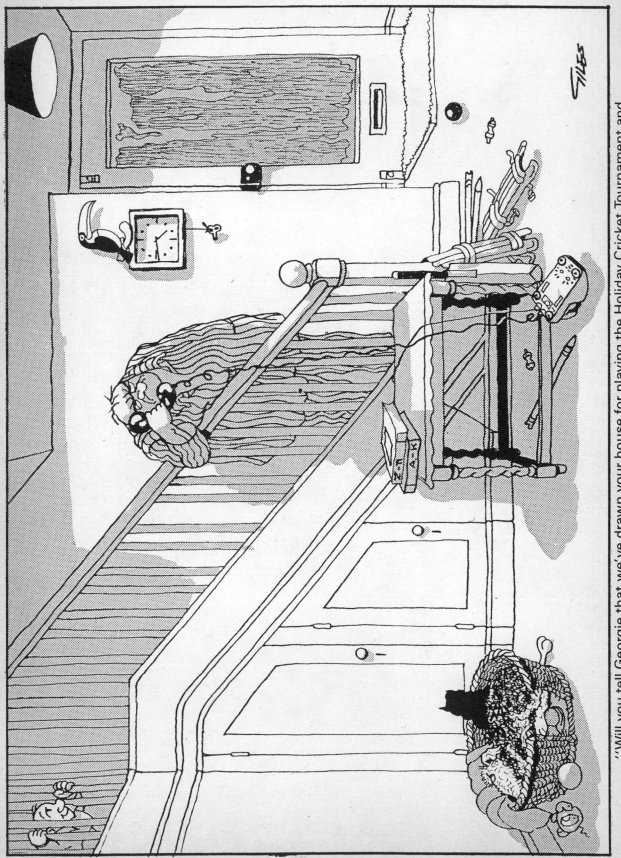

"Will you tell Georgie that we've drawn your house for playing the Holiday Cricket Tournament and we'll all be round in ten minutes."

Daily Express, July 28th, 1987

"Our Florrie doesn't like the Vicar standing her up at the altar."

"You could've waited till we got home before you told them how we voted in the Gallup Poll Survey on Parents' Driving."

(Headline: Gallup Poll decided children prefer mothers' driving)

Daily Express, August 4th, 1987

"My wife's choosing the new drinks dispenser, any bets who doesn't get the job?"

Daily Express, August 6th, 1987

"Ronnie's been in this state of panic since the bottom fell out of the stockmarket."

Sunday Express, August 9th, 1987

"Just now and then I wish Butch would have a go like King Juan Carlos's Alsatian."

(Headline: Royal dog bites Royal dog)

Daily Express, August 11th, 1987

"We know all about Madonna throwing hers into the crowd—put yours back on at once."

Daily Express, August 13th, 1987

"She wants to know what you're going to do about her team's pathetic performance in their first game yesterday."

Sunday Express, August 16th, 1987

"I hear 'Single ticket for Madonna Concert' signed 'besotted fan' is none other than my own lover boy."

Daily Express, August 20th, 1987

"As it is the MCC Bicentenary you could have let Uncle Dennis score just one run in his own garden."

Sunday Express, August 23rd, 1987

"She say you so long coming she let your room to other peoples and you will have to wait at the Airporto, till they are departo."

Daily Express, August 25th, 1987

"Never thought I'd ever see that one so keen to get back to school."

Daily Express, August 27th, 1987

"Dad, remember the gentleman you hit for playing his saxophone all the time we were delayed at Gatwick?"

Sunday Express, August 30th, 1987

"They sure look like they were having one hell of a rave when they were kids."

"Your husband is on No. seven — he can't find the tin-opener, and do you want him to attend your Thursday Post-Natal Class by proxy?"

(Footnote: More wives in the Board room report.)

Daily Express, September 3rd, 1987

"In Belgium your actual trial is not so cosy — they belt you with a piece of pipe and if you say 'Oh' you're guilty."

Daily Express, September 8th, 1987

"Not exactly Four Star but comfy enough to keep him on remand for the England v West Germany match."

Daily Express, September 10th, 1987

"Ah there you are Sergeant, I wonder if I could have Police protection when I call and ask for their Harvest Festival donations."

"She made me write out 200 times: 'I must not consume alcohol during school hours.'"

(Headline: Pub used for emergency classroom)

Daily Express, September 15th, 1987

"'Peter Rabbit' revised might get by — but 'Alice in Bonkerland' might not."

(Headline: Publisher updates 'Peter Rabbit')

Daily Express, September 17th, 1987

"Lying little devil's let me think he's been racing on Sundays ever since we were married."

Sunday Express, September 20th, 1987

"Get that thing out of here or you'll be the one with the tears my boy."

"No AK47 Kalashnikov semi-automatic rifles or Beretta 9mm pistols?"

Daily Express, September 24th, 1987

"First to go soon as I'm a shareholder—me doing all the work and her getting paid for it."

"We've got a right one this time—gives his address as 'Philip, H.R.H., Gatcombe Park.'"

(Headline: 103 m.p.h. Mark Phillips gave Buckingham Palace as address)

Daily Express, October 8th, 1987

"The text today, Ronnie, is about turning the other cheek, not 5 to 2 Bruno takes Bugner in the eighth with a blow to the head."

"It said on the News they'd given up the search for the Loch Ness Monster."

Daily Express, October 13th, 1987

"Ignorant here just asked me 'what is the Commonwealth?' What is the Commonwealth, Sarge?"

Daily Express, October 16th, 1987

"The weathermen forecast that providing we get snow on December 25 it will probably be a white Christmas."

(Footnote: Met Men ignore hurricane warning)

Sunday Express, October 18th, 1987

"Grandma, we don't mind you helping the neighbours clear up their hurricane damage for a fiver, but we do mind you sweeping it into our garden."

Daily Express, October 20th, 1987

"Remember how she flew off the handle last week because I walked across her clean floor with wet feet?"

Daily Express, October 22nd, 1987

"If we're going to bring you hours and hours of Miss World, someone's got to pay for it."

Daily Express, October 29th, 1987

"Sergeant, Colonel says be a good chap and order all other ranks to keep their screams down during his elevenses."

(Footnote: Queen's guards accused of torturing rookies)

Daily Express, November 5th, 1987

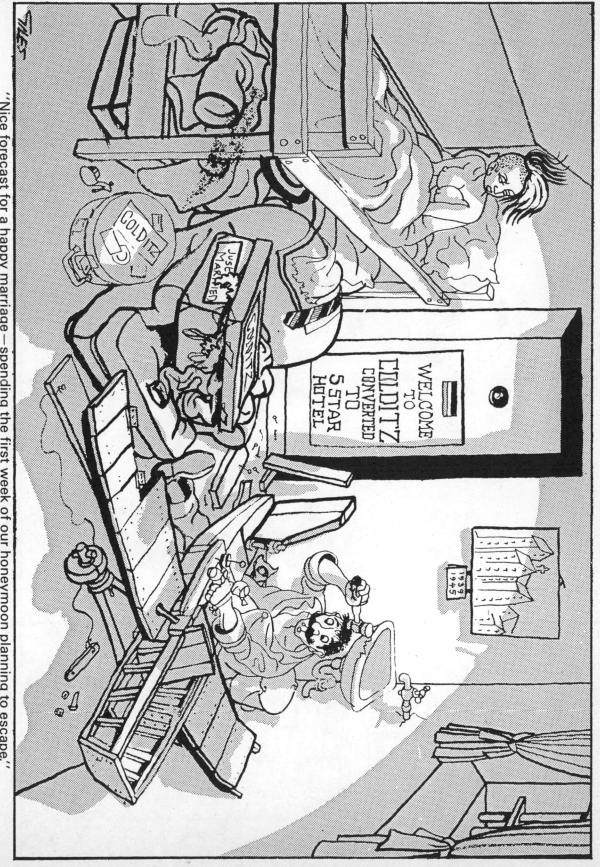

"Nice forecast for a happy marriage — spending the first week of our honeymoon planning to escape."

"Watch it! I can get you 2½ years inside if you hit me just because I nicked your pension book."

Sunday Express, November 15th, 1987

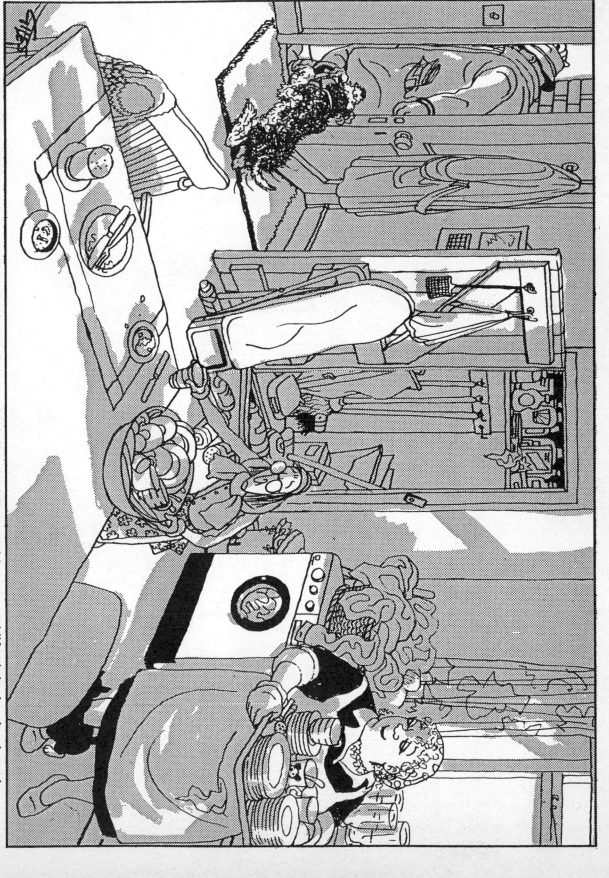

"We sure got sex-equality in this house — he's switched the washing machine on and lifted the ironing board from the cupboard all on his own."

(Footnote: 'Idle' men still rule the roost)

Daily Express, November 17th, 1987

"A gentleman from the postmen's union is waiting for you in the front room."

Daily Express, November 19th, 1987

"Debagging was the least you could expect, Sir—asking them how could they re-pay an overdraft on their salaries."

"I hope you find my prices compare favourably with the Ritz and the Savoy."

Daily Express, November 26th, 1987

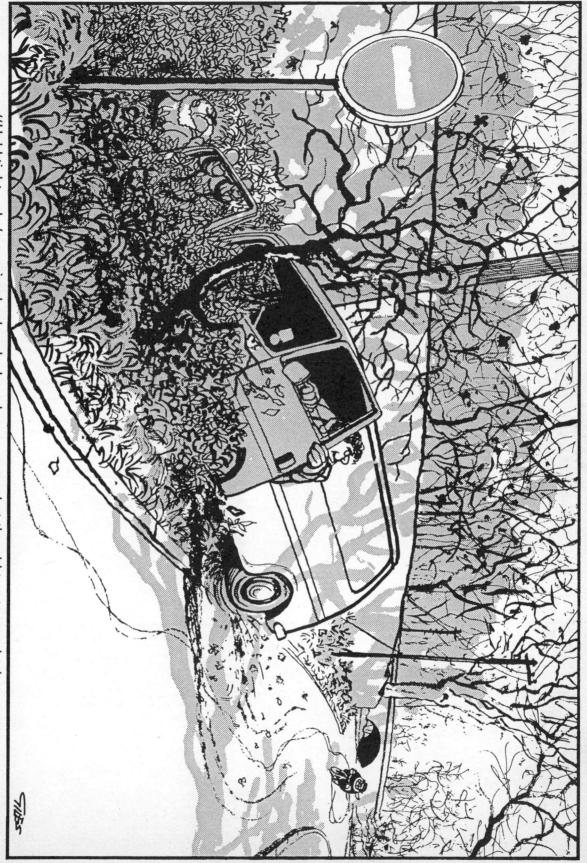

"Hold tight—she's coming back—she heard you say you bet the old trout never had a eye test when you got 'em for free."

(Headline: Free eye tests to end)

Sunday Express, November 29th, 1987

"I should wear your glasses, dear, Mr MacMurphy is in here."

Daily Express, December 1st, 1987

"Well, you'd be doing 90, too, if you had that lot chasing you!"

Daily Express, December 3rd, 1987

"Florence, we appreciate your enthusiasm — and are aware that footballers advertise on their shirts . . ."

Daily Express, December 8th, 1987

"Good news — the builders who started on your storm damage repairs asked me to tell you they'll be back early in the New Year."

"'Noel' louder, please Miss—while they remove Father Christmas for shop-lifting."

Daily Express, December 15th, 1987

"They let us muck about decorating the ward then tell us the hospital's closing down for Christmas!"

Daily Express, December 17th, 1987

"You must expect a few pellets in your backside, Vicar—cutting through here delivering free pheasants to the needy."

Sunday Express, December 20th, 1987

"Another one, Sarg.—"What about Edwina Currie? Her husband drinks and drives.'''

Daily Express, December 22nd, 1987

"Come back the days when you could bundle them all down the pub out of the way."

Daily Express, December 24th, 1987

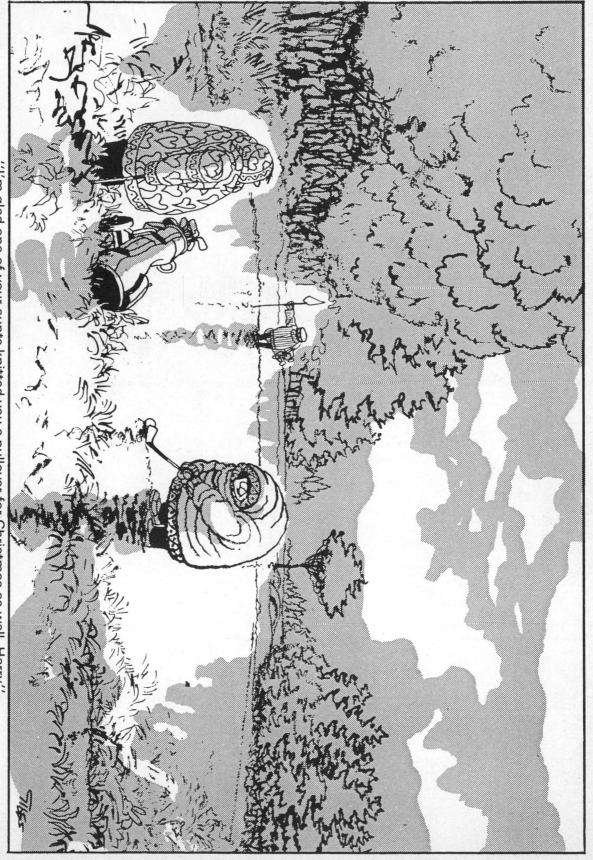

"I'm glad one of your aunts knitted you a pullover for Christmas as well, Harry."

Sunday Express, December 27th, 1987

"Don't tell him he's still wearing it — I think he looks sweet."

Daily Express, December 29th, 1987

"Sorry you've only got three days off to get over New Year's Eve after a gruelling three-day week on top of your long Christmas holiday."

Daily Express, December 31st, 1987

"Do you think we should tell Vicar he's got a grandma in his pear tree?"

Sunday Express, January 3rd, 1983

"Ahoy, there—I hope you haven't forgotten you're taking us all to the preview of the Boat Show today."

Daily Express, January 5th, 1988

"I'll handle Horatio Nelson here, you fend off Captain Bligh."

Daily Express, January 7th, 1988

"Just turn your back for a few hours strike and they're off."

"It would be advisable for one and all to make a mental note that your failures would cost me MY holiday."

Daily Express, January 12th, 1988

"Fare charges still going up—12p for a fish to go by bus."

(Footnote: A boy was in fact charged 12p fare for a fish this week)

Sunday Express, January 17th, 1988

"If you don't soon go to sleep you could end up in a little basket on Princess Diana's doorstep, my lady."

(Headline: Princess Diana would like a baby daughter!)

Daily Express, January 21st, 1988

"Every year we're not going to have this lark again—we're going to make our own snowplough. He's off to start one right now."

"Wait till you see your 'agony aunt' before you start writing."

Daily Express, January 28th, 1988

"I'd gladly give up decorating the living room so Vera could have her new gold tooth."

"You asked for that—'Funny comic nose, Madam? Oh, I see you've already got one!'"

Daily Express, February 2nd, 1988

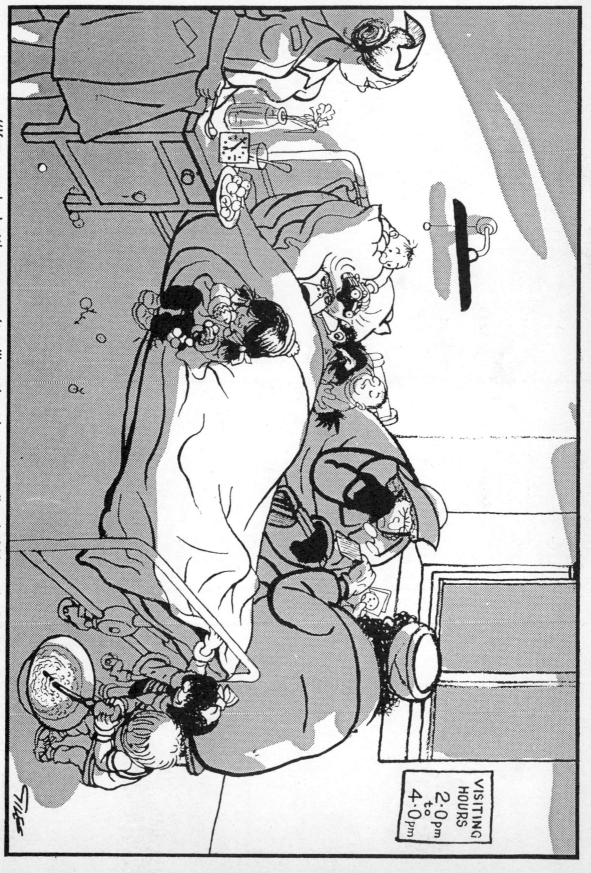

"If my regular battleaxe wasn't gallivanting about on strike she'd have had this lot out of here sharp on the dot."

Daily Express, February 4th, 1988

"Your wife won't be happy in the new house—you taking the wrong road with the furniture and spending the weekend down here."

Sunday Express, February 7th, 1988

"Right, I've just sold the TV set!"

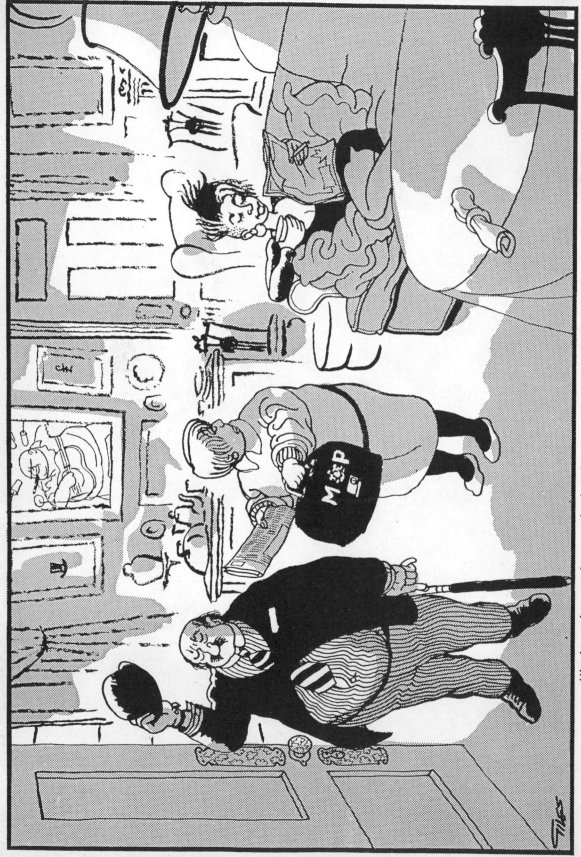

"It doesn't surprise me the Leader doesn't want TV cameras in the House."

Daily Express, February 11th, 1988

"One way to get a 'Highly Commended' — buy a Monroe blouse from Sotheby's and send a Valentine card to all the judges."

Sunday Express, February 14th, 1988

"Grandma! The French Premier swearing at Mrs Thatcher does not mean you can use that word in front of the children."

Daily Express, February 16th, 1988

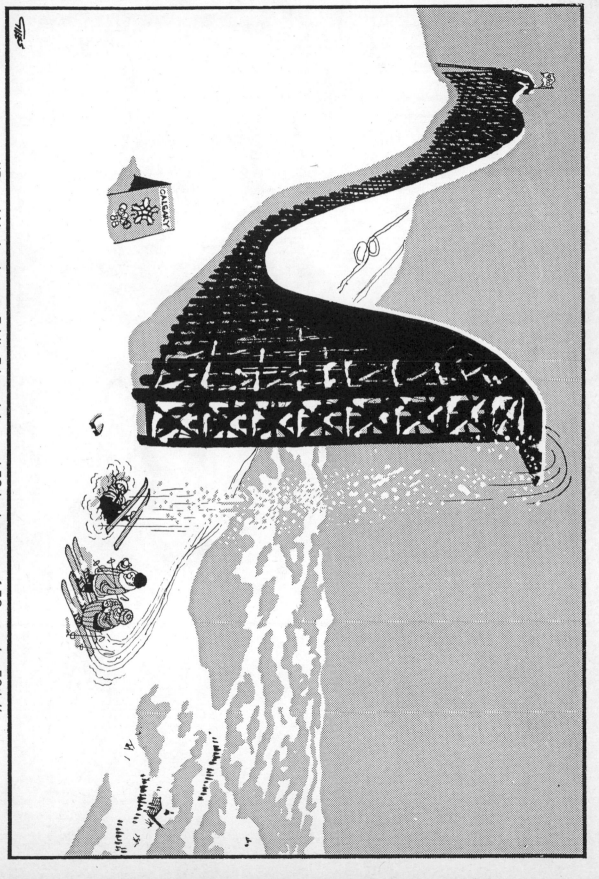

"Bravo! You've beaten Eddie Edwards' record 58th place out of 58—you're 59th."

Daily Express, February 18th, 1988

"Our ski jumper is not the only one good at being last."

Sunday Express, February 21st, 1988

"Another excuse for not going on holiday — if they can get past the Brigade of Guards how can we leave our house empty for two weeks."

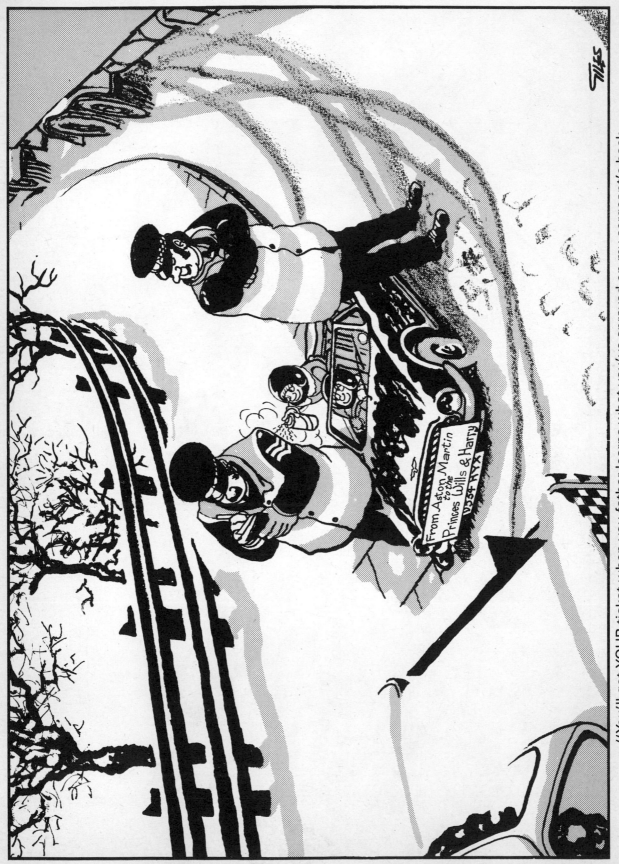

"You'll get YOUR ticket when you father learns what you've sprayed on my sergeant's back, Your Royal Highness."

"It's your ex-wife, she's heard you're becoming a rock star but she can't find you listed in the 200 millionaires."

Sunday Express, February 28th, 1988

"I know it's Leap Year, but I think we should wait a little while before we take out the licence."

Daily Express, March 1st, 1988

"I fear secrets of an ex-chambermaid of Mrs Higgins of Arcadia Avenue wouldn't attract the readers as much as the secrets of an ex-chambermaid from Balmoral."

"I can see the headline, Vera—'Amorous GP tells sexy patient to take her hat off.'"

(Headline: Naked GP's surgery sex-romps taped)

Sunday Express, March 6th, 1988

"Sorry, Sir, you're in the wrong county. We only supply a bag without the buns."

"I understand you wish to arrange a mortgage for you to acquire a small flower in a pot for Mother's Day this coming Sunday."

Daily Express, March 10th, 1988

"Now we come to the bit where Father's come out without any money and Mother pays."

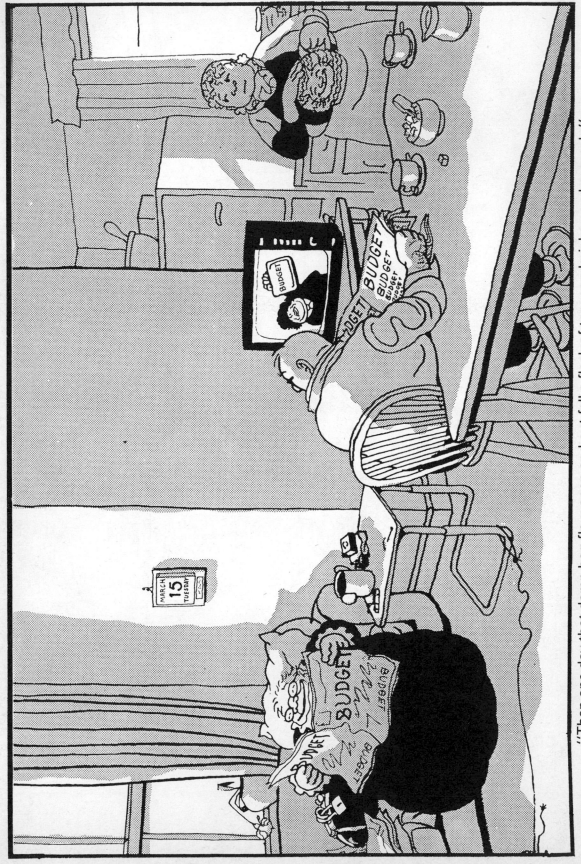

"Then one day that damn bag flew open and out fell a flask of tea, sandwiches and an apple."

Daily Express, March 15th, 1988

"Our tax bonanza—all gone, Mummy!"

Daily Express, March 17th, 1988

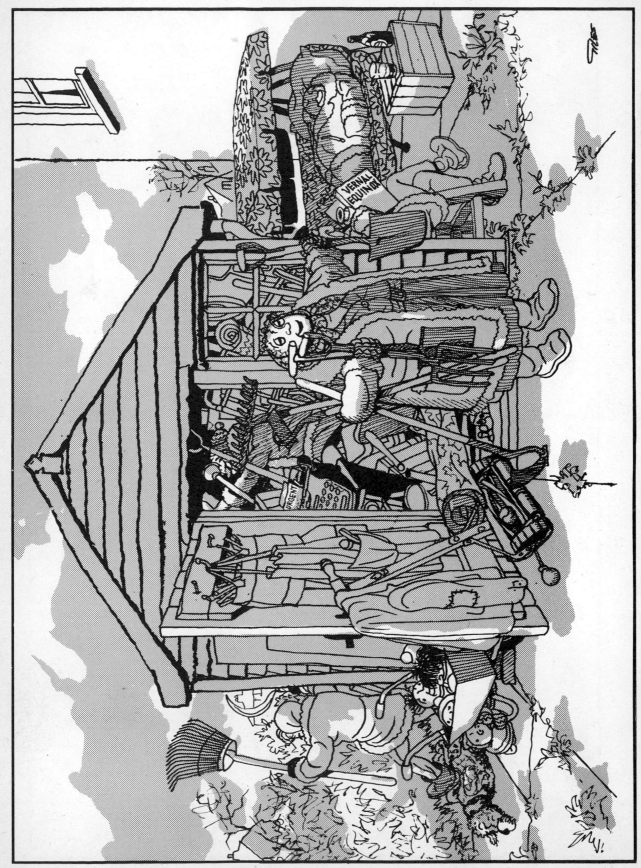

"When I said it's time we got the garden things out for Spring I was thinking more in the line of these."

Sunday Express, March 20th, 1988

"Here she comes — "What's all this about the French saying our bangers are rancid, gristly, and a week old before she gets them?'"

Daily Express, March 22nd, 1988

"These are no good—they make them ticklish."

Daily Express, March 24th, 1988

"Out of a truck-load of mahogany your husband should be able to make a couple of decent egg racks for Easter."

Sunday Express, March 27th, 1988

"My dream honeymoon — sitting freezing for three days while you play midfield for a knock-up team to pass the time."

Sunday Express, April 3rd, 1988

"You've caddied for us for years without borrowing ideas from Ian Botham!"

Sunday Express, April 10th, 1988

"Porky says no slippers till you've taken him for his walkies."

Sunday Express, April 17th, 1988

"Worse than getting the children back to school—getting him back to the Commons the morning after he has voted against Maggie."

Daily Express, April 19th, 1988

"You'll only be guarding the knives, forks and spoons etc—Her Majesty and HRH have gone to Australia."

(Headline: Australians take over guard at Buckingham Palace)

Daily Express, April 21st, 1988

"I've made dinner for four o'clock—I thought your new three o'clock closing time law had started."

"You don't have this problem of your children not recognising you because you spend too much time at the office."

Daily Express, April 26th, 1988

"Just bought £2.1 billion worth of Rowntree shares and not eating your Kit Kat?"

Daily Express, April 28th, 1988

"Looks as if we're going to be here for a long time—how about joining in singing The Merry Month of May?"

Sunday Express, May 1st, 1988

"It's the only arithmetic they know."

"Never mind about 'Princess Diana jumped it in one' — I know me rules."

(Headline: Princess Diana leapt from train naming ceremony)

Daily Express, May 5th, 1988

"You don't encourage your dad very much telling him that's more than he's scored in his whole life."

Sunday Express, May 8th, 1988

"If the experts are right your daughter's marriage has a good chance of survival."

Daily Express, May 10th, 1988

"You're wasting your time, cat—the most she'll leave you is her lucky charm and half a bottle of peppermints."

"Tell Daddy some gentlemen are here to see him about the 50—1 Wimbledon to win the Cup he was giving them yesterday."

Sunday Express, May 15th, 1988

"Apart from a note saying 'Over to you' there's a bill for massaging a bad back."

(Headline: More top people using sex parlours)

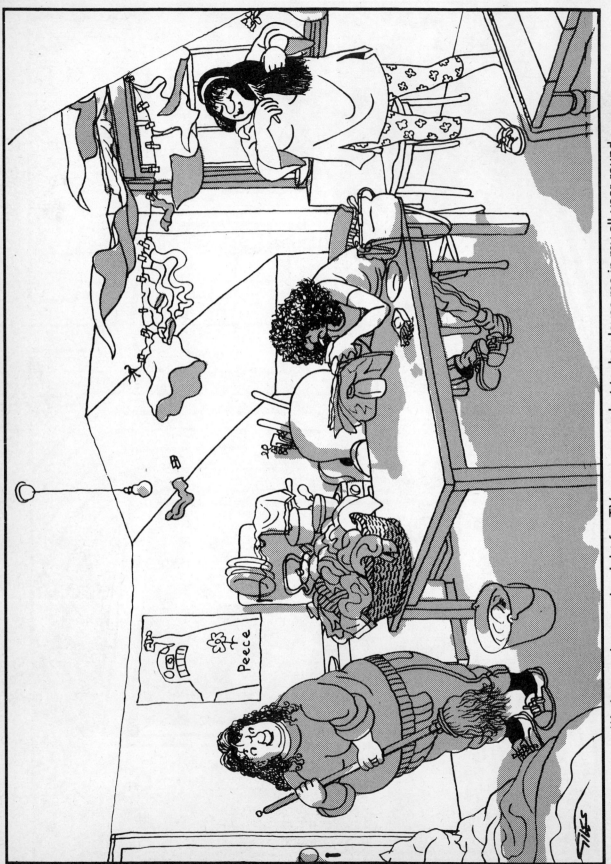

"A dress a day may be right for TV announcers but toyboy loves me in my all-year-round Yves St Laurent jeans and pullover."

Daily Express, May 19th, 1988

"You don't think my wife's going to believe some rotter stole my trousers while I was at a poll tax debate."

(Headline: MP's sex romp in Commons shower)

Sunday Express, May 22nd, 1988

"As this aerial picture shows quite clearly—a kidney-shaped pool, a large block of garages, extensive stables and paddocks, far-reaching acreage . . ."

Daily Express, May 24th, 1988

"We appreciate you're new here but should Her Majesty look in again please don't ask Her if Her ticket is 'legit' or did she get it on the market."

Daily Express, May 26th, 1988

"I know just what you're going to say — it's a teeny bit bigger than you had planned."

Sunday Express, May 29th, 1988

"It's keep Chelsea out of Moscow or bye-bye Glasnost."

"The vandals who threw eggs at your horse yesterday — the Community Service Order people have sent them to clean him up."

Daily Express, June 2nd, 1988

"Before you go celebrating Mr Reagan's Dawn of a Brave New Era, the drain at the back of the chickens shed's blocked."

"If Edwina Currie's right this time you'll be able to have all your little tumours and ulcers done right here while you wait."

Daily Express, June 7th, 1988

"He asked the Prince if he had ever personally experienced any of Her Royal Highness's backhand."

"How do you think I feel in front of the neighbours? You the only one in the team not charged with indecent behaviour."

Sunday Express, June 12th, 1988